IF CREATORS ARE LIKE WIZARDS

First paperback edition September 2021

ISBN 978-1-7377156-0-3

Published by Jamie and Ash Publishing.

www.jamierusso.me
www.ashlamb.com

IF CREATORS ARE LIKE

WIZARDS

JAMIE RUSSO   ASH LAMB

If creators are like wizards...

then pencils are like magic wands.

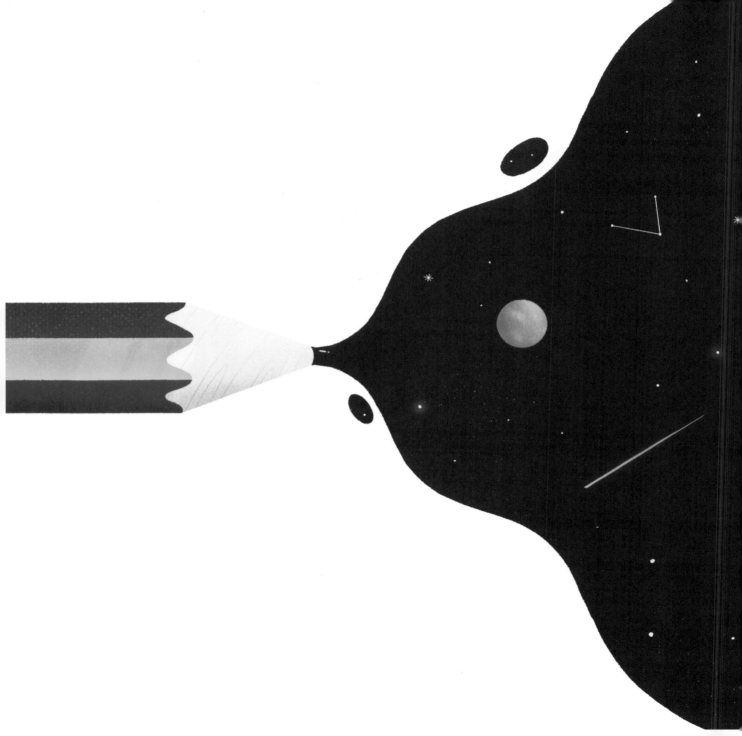

Sprinkle a little pixie dust and POOF!

A remarkable new universe.

Ideas are like rocket ships,

transport us to outer space.

Pencils are like pyramids.

Ticonderogas touch the sky.

Notebooks are like a collection of life stories,
memories are worth more than gold.

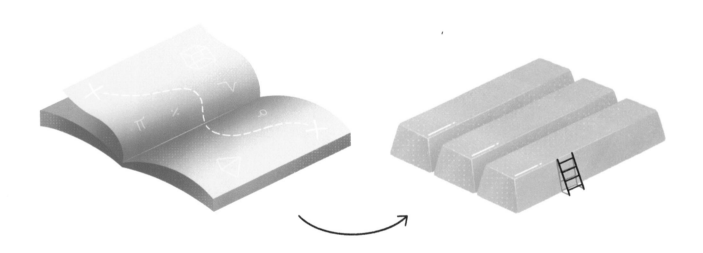

Movies are like shooting stars.

Illuminate the silver screen.

THEN

NOW

A writer plants ideas like seeds,
that grow taller than a redwood tree.

An architect transforms neighborhoods,

a masterpiece in the street.

A sailor climbs aboard a sailboat,

the start of a magical adventure.

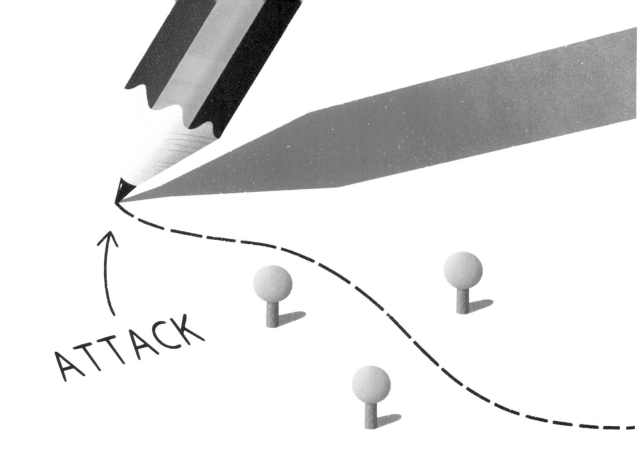

When an artist sketches formations,

an idea army marches into battle.

Chefs experiment with ingredients,

the perfect recipe is a dash of salt away.

SALT

SUGAR

PENCIL

TOMATO

AVOCADO

FISH

An honorable man once explained, "I have a dream,"

a reminder that words of hope reverberate.

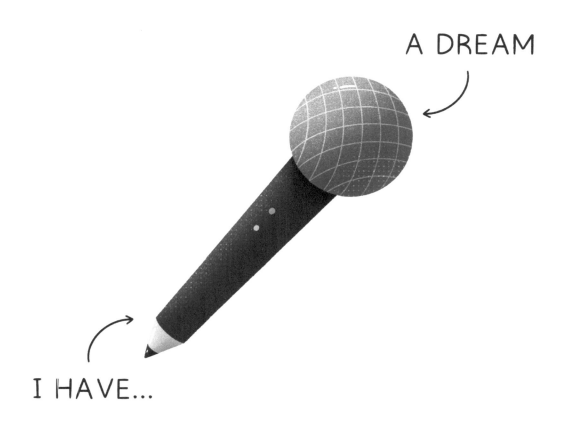

A DREAM

I HAVE...

Today we have computers, artificial intelligence, and productivity hacks.

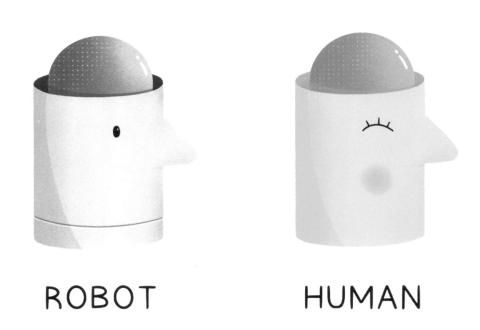

ROBOT   HUMAN

To withstand the test of time, creators need three things: pencil, heart, and mind.

PENCIL   HEART   MIND

Jamie Russo is a writer based in Brooklyn, NY.
He is the author of a collection of short stories for
aspiring creators. His debut title, The Underdog Paradox,
is a #1 Amazon Bestseller.

 jamierusso.me   @jamierusso

Ash Lamb is an illustrator based in Barcelona, Spain.
He shares visual stories and ideas from his life journey
to help others navigate their own. He firmly believes that
the power of storytelling can change the world.

 ashlamb.com   @ash_lmb

CPSIA information can be obtained
at www.ICGtesting.com
Printed in the USA
LVHW070933270821
696093LV00019B/103